The Specialist

By

Charles (Chic) Sale

America's great rural
character actor

Publishers:
Specialist Publishing Company
Wainwright Building
St. Louis, Mo.

Ninth Printing

LEM PUTT—that wasn't his real name—really lived. He was just as sincere in his work as a great painter whose heart is in his canvas; and in this little sketch I have simply tried to bring to you recollections of a man I once knew, who was so rich in odd and likable traits of character as to make a most lasting impression on my memory.

CHARLES (CHIC) SALE.

DOC SALE'S BOY

There's Chic Sale, Doc Sale's boy
From Urbana, Illinoy,
Where he worked, boy an' man
'Till he found a *better* plan;
Jist rigged up a lot o' jokes,
Then he started ape-in' fokes—
Hometown fokes—their speech or whim
Come as natural-like t' him!
He kin take-off you or me
Right down to a tee-y-tee
'Till our kinfokes say: "Blamedon,
That's like *you!*" or "Jist like John!"

                Gentle, too;
Not like play-act fellers do—
Others of 'em—who proclaim
Somethin' kin to mortal shame
'Cause a feller's country-bred—
Ignorance, I've always said!
Chic, though, he jist ripples on,
Smiles and swears a soft "Doggone!"
Then he speckylates on who
God made *first,* us fokes or you
City fokes; and by an' by
He'll declare the vote a tie—
Says he thinks we *both* are good
If we're only understood—
That's Chic Sale!

                    Just ripples on
'Bout the home fokes, or doggone
Barnyard scene, some ginny hens,
Hair-lipped fokes an' family wens,
"Literarys", patunt rights,
Sun-kissed days and silver nights;
Paw-paws an' the far off "cheep"
Comin' from the ol' well-sweep
Down through memry; puncheon floors
Outside latch an' friendly doors;
Chink vines, too, an' garden sass
All mixed up with hollyhocks—
Everything!—until, I jocks,
J jist pine t' pull up stakes
An' go back for their sweet sakes!

                    Donblame his hide!
Laffed at him until I've *cried*
Lots o' times, an' never know
Why on earth I take on so!—
Mebbe it's his brand o' jokes,
Or his knack of ape-in' fokes,
Or—like enuff—he brings to mind
Things I've loved *an' left behind!*

              John D. Wells, in the
                Buffalo Courier-Express.

Foreword

Humor, when enjoyed to the full, is that which is based upon events, experiences, or intimate knowledge of the subject described; or a mixture of all three. And if the subject is one which is not usually discussed, yet is of a character incident to the home life of each family, that, also, adds to the zest with which one listens to the story told; or if printed, intensifies the interest of the reader.

In "The Specialist" is sought to portray generally-known-but-seldom-mentioned incidents of every day life.

And what could be a better vehicle for the presentation than the voluble and cock-sure specialist? We have all met the super-serious individual, utterly devoid of the sense of humor, on whose shoulders rests the responsibility for the success of your business and mine. Out of his unwarranted seriousness—to those who recognize the artfulness of the visionary—comes mirth, and laughter and—side-aches.

This little story has been spoken by the author to numerously attended gatherings in different sections of the country for several years past—to the great delight of his hearers. It has been put in permanent form at the suggestion of many friends, with whom the author joins in the hope that it may afford some measure of enjoyment to those under whose eye it may fall.

W. S. McCLEVEY.

St. Louis, January, 1929.

The Specialist

Mr. President and Gentlemen:

You've heerd a lot of pratin' and prattlin' about this bein' the age of specialization. I'm a carpenter by trade. At one time I could of built a house, barn, church or chicken coop. But I seen the need of a specialist in my line, so I studied her. I got her; she's mine. Gentlemen, you are face to face with the champion privy builder of Sangamon County.

Luke Harkins was my first customer. He heerd about me specializin' and decided to take a chance. I built fer him just the average eight family, three holer. With that job my reputation was made, and since then I have devoted all my time and thought to that special line. Of course, when business is slack, I do do a little paperhangin' on the side. But my heart is just in privy buildin'. And when I finish a job, I ain't through. I give all my customers six months' privy service free gratis. I explained this to Luke, and one day he calls me up and sez: "Lem, I wish you'd come out here; I'm havin' privy trouble."

So I gits in the car and drives out to Luke's place, and hid behind them Baldwins, where I could get a good view of the situation.

It was right in the middle of hayin' time, and them hired hands was goin' in there and stayin' anywheres from forty minutes to an hour. Think of that!

I sez: "Luke, you sure have got privy trouble." So I takes out my kit of tools and goes in to examine the structure.

First I looks at the catalogue hangin' there, thinkin' it might be that; but it wasn't even from a reckonized house.

Then I looks at the seats proper, and I see what the trouble was. I had made them holes too durn comfortable. So I gets out a scroll saw and cuts 'em square with hard edges. Then I go back and takes up my position as before—me here, the Baldwins here, and the privy there. And I watched them hired hands goin' in and out for nearly two hours; and not one of them was stayin' more than four minutes.

"Luke," I sez, "I've solved her." That's what comes of bein' a specialist, gentlemen.

'Twarn't long after I built that twin job for the school house, and then after that the biggest plant up to date—a eight holer. Elmer Ridgway was down and looked it over. And he come to me one day and sez: "Lem, I seen that eight hole job you done down there at the Corners, and it sure is a dandy; and figgerin' as how I'm goin' to build on the old Robinson property, I thought I'd ask you to kind of estimate on a job for me."

"You come to the right man, Elmer," I sez. "I'll be out as soon as I get the roof on the two-seater I'm puttin' up for the Sheriff."

Couple of days later I drives out to Elmer's place, gettin' there about dinner time. I knocks a couple of times on the door and I see they got a lot of folks to dinner, so not wishin' to disturb 'em, I just sneaks around to the side door and yells, "Hey, Elmer, here I am; where do you want that privy put?"

Elmer comes out and we get to talkin' about a good location. He was all fer puttin' her right alongside a jagged path runnin' by a big Northern Spy.

"I wouldn't do it, Elmer," I sez; "and I'll tell you why. In the first place, her bein' near a tree is bad. There ain't no sound in nature so disconcertin' as the sound of apples droppin' on th' roof. Then

"Some of them stayed nearly an
hour"

another thing, there's a crooked path runnin' by that tree and the soil there ain't adapted to absorbin' moisture. Durin' the rainy season she's likely to be slippery. Take your grandpappy—goin' out there is about the only recreation he gets. He'll go out some rainy night with his nighties flappin' around his legs, and like as not when you come out in the mornin' you'll find him prone in the mud, or maybe skidded off one of them curves and wound up in the corn crib. No, sir," I sez, "put her in a straight line with the house and if it's all the same to you have her go past the woodpile. I'll tell you why.

"Take a woman, fer instance—out she goes. On the way back she'll gather five sticks of wood, and the average woman will make four or five trips a day. There's twenty sticks in the wood box without any trouble. On the other hand, take a timid woman, if she sees any men folks around, she's too bashful to go direct out so she'll go to the wood-pile, pick up the wood, go back to the house and watch her chance. The average timid woman — especially a new hired girl—I've knowed to make as many as ten trips to the wood-pile before she goes in, regardless. On a good day you'll have your wood box filled by noon, and right there is a savin' of time.

"Now, about the diggin' of her. You can't be too careful about that," I sez; "dig her deep and dig her wide. It's a mighty sight better to have a little privy over a big hole than a big privy over a little hole. Another thing; when you dig her deep you've got 'er dug; and you ain't got that disconcertin' thought stealin' over you that sooner or later you'll have to dig again.

"And when it comes to construction," I sez, "I can give you joists or beams. Joists make a good job. Beams cost a bit more, but they're worth it. Beams, you might say, will last forever. 'Course, I could give you joists, but take your Aunt Emmy, she ain't gettin' a mite lighter. Some day she might be out there when them joists give way and there she'd be—catched. Another thing you've got to figger on, Elmer," I sez, "is that Odd Fellows picnic in the fall. Them boys is goin' to get in there in fours and sixes, singin' and drinkin', and the like, and I want to tell you there's nothin' breaks up an Odd Fellows picnic quicker than a diggin' party. Beams, I say, every time, and rest secure.

"And about her roof," I sez. "I can give you a lean-to type or a pitch roof. Pitch roofs cost a little more, but some of our best people has lean-tos. If it was fer myself, I'd have a lean-to, and I'll tell you why.

"A lean-to has two less corners fer the wasps to build their nests in; and on a hot August afternoon there ain't nothin'

so disconcertin' as a lot of wasps buzzin'
'round while you're settin' there doin' a
little readin', figgerin', or thinkin'. Another thing," I sez, "a lean-to gives you a
high door. Take that son of yours, shoot-
in' up like a weed; don't any of him seem
to be turnin' under. If he was tryin' to
get under a pitch roof door he'd crack his
head everytime. Take a lean-to, Elmer;
they ain't stylish, but they're practical.

"Now, about her furnishin's. I can give
you a nail or hook for the catalogue, and
besides, a box for cobs. You take your
pa, for instance; he's of the old school and
naturally he'd prefer the box; so put 'em
both in, Elmer. Won't cost you a bit more
for the box and keeps peace in the family.
You can't teach an old dog new tricks,"
I sez.

"And as long as we're on furnishin's,
I'll tell you about a technical point that
was put to me the other day. The question was this: 'What is the life, or how

long will the average mail order catalogue last, in just the plain, ordinary eight family three holer?' It stumped me for a spell; but this bein' a reasonable question I checked up, and found that by placin' the catalogue in there, say in January —when you get your new one—you should be into the harness section by June; but, of course, that ain't through apple time, and not countin' on too many city visitors, either.

"An' another thing—they've been puttin' so many of those stiff colored sheets in the catalogue here lately that it makes it hard to figger. Somethin' really ought to be done about this, and I've thought about takin' it up with Mr. Sears Roebuck hisself.

"As to the latch fer her, I can give you a spool and string, or a hook and eye. The cost of a spool and string is practically nothin', but they ain't positive in action. If somebody comes out and starts rattlin'

"If it was me, Elmer, I'd say no windows;
and I'll tell you why."

the door, either the spool or the string is apt to give way, and there you are. But, with a hook and eye she's yours, you might say, for the whole afternoon, if you're so minded. Put on the hook and eye of the best quality 'cause there ain't nothin' that'll rack a man's nerves more than to be sittin' there ponderin', without a good, strong, substantial latch on the door." And he agreed with me.

"Now," I sez, "what about windows; some want 'em, some don't. They ain't so popular as they used to be. If it was me, Elmer, I'd say no windows; and I'll tell you why. Take, fer instance, somebody comin' out—maybe they're just in a hurry or maybe they waited too long. If the door don't open right away and you won't answer 'em, nine times out of ten they'll go 'round and 'round and look in the window, and you don't get the privacy you ought to.

"Now, about ventilators, or the designs

I cut in the doors. I can give you stars, diamonds, or crescents—there ain't much choice—all give good service. A lot of people like stars, because they throw a ragged shadder. Others like crescents 'cause they're graceful and simple. Last year we was cuttin' a lot of stars; but this year people are kinda quietin' down and runnin' more to crescents. I do cut twinin' hearts now and then for young married couples; and bunches of grapes for the newly rich. These last two 'designs come under the head of novelties and I don't very often suggest 'em, because it takes time and runs into money.

"I wouldn't take any snap judgment on her ventilators, Elmer," I sez, "because they've got a lot to do with the beauty of the structure. And don't over-do it, like Doc Turner did. He wanted stars and crescents both, against my better judgment, and now he's sorry. But it's too late; 'cause when I cut 'em, they're cut." And, gentlemen, you can get mighty tired, sittin' day after day lookin' at a ventilator that ain't to your likin'.

"Now," I sez, "how do you want that door to swing? Openin' in or out? He said he didn't know. So I sez it should open in. This is the way it works out: Place yourself in there. The door openin' in, say about forty-five degree. This gives you air and lets the sun beat in. Now, if you hear anybody comin', you can give it a quick shove with your foot and there you are. But if she swings out, where are you? You can't run the risk of havin' her open for air or sun, because if anyone comes, you can't get up off that seat, reach way around and grab 'er without gettin' caught, now can you? He could see I was right."

So I built his door like all my doors, swingin' in, and, of course, facing east, to get the full benefit of th' sun. And I tell you, gentlemen, there ain't nothin' more restful than to get out there in the mornin', comfortably seated, with th' door about three-fourths open. The old sun, beatin' in on you, sort of relaxes a body— makes you feel m-i-g-h-t-y, m-i-g-h-t-y r-e-s-t-f-u-l.

"Now," I sez, "about the paintin' of her. What color do you want 'er, Elmer?" He said red. "Elmer," I sez, "I can paint her red, and red makes a beautiful job; or I can paint her a bright green, or any one of a half dozen other colors, and they're all mighty pretty; but it ain't practical to use a single solid color, and I'll tell you why. She's too durn hard to see at night. You need contrast—just like they use on them railroad crossin' bars—so you can see 'em in the dark.

"If I was you, I'd paint her a bright red, with white trimmin's—just like your barn. Then she'll match up nice in the daytime, and you can spot 'er easy at night, when you ain't got much time to go scoutin' around.

"There's a lot of fine points to puttin' up a first-class privy that the average man don't think about. It's no job for an amachoor, take my word on it. There's a whole lot more to it than you can see by just takin' a few squints at your nabor's. Why, one of the worst tragedies around here in years was because old man Clark's boys thought they knowed somethin' about this kind of work, and they didn't.

"Old man Clark—if he's a day he's ninety-seven—lives over there across the holler with his boys. Asked me to come over and estimate on their job. My price was too high; so they decided to do it themselves. And that's where the trouble begun.

"I was doin' a little paper hangin' at the time for that widder that lives down past the old creamery. As I'd drive by I could see the boys a-workin'. Of course, I didn't want to butt in, so used to just holler at 'em on the way by and say, naborly like: 'Hey, boys, see you're doin' a little buildin'.' You see, I didn't want to act like I was buttin' in on their work; but I knowed all the time they was goin' to have trouble with that privy. And they did. From all outside appearance it was a regulation job, but not being experienced along this line, they didn't anchor her.

"You see, I put a 4 by 4 that runs from the top right straight on down five foot into the ground. That's why you never see any of my jobs upset Hallowe'en night. They might *pull* 'em out, but they'll never upset 'em.

"Here's what happened: They didn't anchor theirs, and they painted it solid red—two bad mistakes.

"Hallowe'en night come along, darker than pitch. Old man Clark was out in there. Some of them devilish nabor boys

was out for no good, and they upset 'er
with the old man in it.

"Of course, the old man got to callin'
and his boys heard the noise. One of
'em sez: 'What's the racket? Somebody
must be at the chickens.' So they took
the lantern, started out to the chicken
shed. They didn't find anything wrong
there, and they started back to the house.
Then they heerd the dog bark, and one of
his boys sez, 'Sounds like that barkin' is
over towards the privy.' It bein' painted
red, they couldn't see she was upset, so
they started over there.

"In the meantime the old man had
gotten so confused that he started to
crawl out through the hole, yellin' for
help all the time. The boys reckonized
his voice and come runnin', but just as
they got there he lost his holt and fell.
After that they just *called* — didn't go
near him. So you see what a tragedy that
was; and they tell me he has been prac-

tically ostercized from society ever since."

Well, time passed, and I finally got Elmer's job done; and, gentlemen, everybody says that, next to my eight holer, it's the finest piece of construction work in the county.

Sometimes, when I get to feelin' blue and thinkin' I hitched my wagon to the wrong star, and maybe I should have took up chiropracty or veternary, I just pack the little woman and the kids in the back of my car and start out, aimin' to fetch up at Elmer's place along about dusk.

When we gets to the top of the hill overlookin' his place, we stops. I slips the gear in mutual, and we jest sit there lookin' at that beautiful sight. There sits that privy on that knoll near the woodpile, painted red and white, mornin' glories growin' up over her and Mr. Sun bathin' her in a burst of yeller color as he drops back of them hills. You can hear the dog barkin' in the distance, bringin' the cows up fer milkin', and the slow squeak of Elmer's windmill pumpin' away day after day the same as me.

As I look at that beautiful picture of my work, I'm proud. I heaves a sigh of satisfaction, my eyes fill up and I sez to myself, "Folks are right when they say that next to my eight holer that's the finest piece of construction work I ever done. I know I done right in Specializin'; I'm sittin' on top of the world; and I hope that boy of mine who is growin' up like a weed keeps up the good work when I'm gone."

With one last look as we pulls away, I slips my arm around the Missus and I sez, "Nora, Elmer don't have to worry, he's a boy that's got hisself a privy, a m-i-g-h-t-y, m-i-g-h-t-y, p-r-e-t-t-y p-r-i-v-y."

Thank you, gentlemen.

The Cup Overfloweth